Contents

In this comic ...

Billy

Little sis

Shazam!

Billy and his little sis were normal kids.

Well, **I** am normal!

Look who is talking!

One day Billy met a wizard called Shazam.

Say my name and you will transform!

Shazam!

Now Billy is Captain Marvel. He has super powers!

When Billy's little sis calls out SHAZAM ...

Shazam!

... she transforms too!

I am small ...

... but speedy!

An Awkward Job

Billy works on a television show.

Morning all!

I laughed when I saw yesterday's show, Billy!

Fantastic stories on Captain Marvel!

Hey! The ball on that crane is out of control!

Look, Billy!

Billy?

But Billy was off!

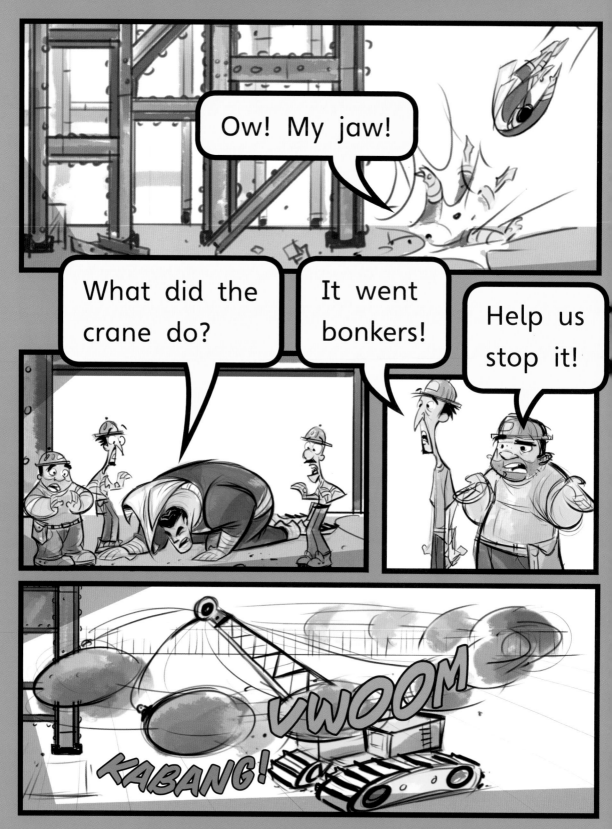

14

15